Some of us

by Ljiljana Rylands
illustrated by the author

edited by Sarah Allen

Published by Dinosaur Publications

Some of us are short and fat,

others thin and tall.

Some of us have lots of hair,

others none at all.

Some of us just love a mess,

others are quite neat.

Some of us walk round the town,

some use wheels not feet.

Some of us have black skin,

some of us have white.

Some of us eat lots of meat,

some don't think it's right.

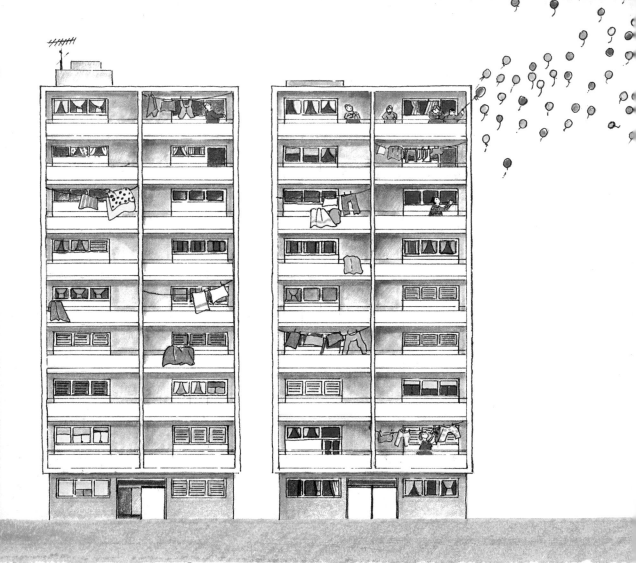

Some of us live up on high,

others on the ground.

Some of us make lots of noise,

others not a sound.

Some of us go out in crowds,

others are alone.

Some of us go out to work,

others work at home.

Some of us will rush about,

some of us are lazy.

Some of us are sensible,

some of us are crazy.

Text and illustrations copyright © Ljiljana Rylands 1985

Published by Dinosaur Publications
a member of the Collins Group
8 Grafton Street, London, W1X 3LA

Printed by Warners of Bourne and London